CARL MARIA VON WEBER

KONZERTSTÜCK

F minor/f-Moll/Fa mineur
WeV N.17

Edited by/Herausgegeben von
Markus Bandur

Ernst Eulenburg Ltd

London · Mainz · Madrid · New York · Paris · Prague · Tokyo · Toronto · Zürich

CONTENTS

Critical edition based on
Carl Maria von Weber. Complete Works
Volume V/5
© 2018 Schott Music GmbH & Co. KG, Mainz
WGA 1055, ISMN 979-0-001-15653-0
Reprinted by permission

© 2019 Ernst Eulenburg & Co GmbH, Mainz
for Europe excluding the British Isles
Ernst Eulenburg Ltd, London
for all other countries

Ernst Eulenburg Ltd
48 Great Marlborough Street
London W1F 7BB

PREFACE

Weber's *Konzertstück* [Concert Piece] for Piano and Orchestra has a special position within the composer's oeuvre as well as within the genre history of the Romantic piano concerto. This has to do not only with the work's great technical demands on the pianist, but also with its innovative expressive character and, notably, with its musico-poetic form developed from a programmatic idea.

The reliance of the customised formal design on a programmatic idea can, in fact, be likewise found around 1820 – albeit to a clearly lesser extent – in works, for instance, by Louis Spohr, Daniel Steibelt, John Field and Ferdinand Ries. Yet, especially in the 19th century and – including the formal shape of Igor Stravinsky's *Capriccio* for Piano and Orchestra – also in the 20th century, Weber's *Konzertstück* was the starting point for the denouement of the standardised cyclical form and for the manifestation of the one-movement concerto form.

At the beginning of March 1815, shortly after Weber had received the specimen exemplars of his second piano concerto, he was already thinking of another, third concerto for piano and orchestra in F minor. Revealing in this conjunction are his reflections in his letter to Friedrich Rochlitz of 14 March 1815, extending beyond this project, on the use of minor keys in concert works and for programme music in general. His letter makes it clear that indeed he was not a devotee of such 'captioned musical pictures', programme music, that is, and even viewed their advocates as 'musical charlatans'. Certainly, he is of the opinion that concertos in the minor would be less effective than those in the major. But for this reason he is hoping that the narrative 'imposing' itself on him in his compositional plans for the third piano concerto, i.e., the 'kind of story' that underlies the work in the form of "titles", would compensate the audience for this disadvantage:

'I'm now planning a *piano concerto* in *F minor*, but since the *minor concertos* are seldom effective with the audience without a certain inspiring concept, then so strangely and involuntarily foisted upon me as a whole is a kind of story, according to the thread of which the piece is arranged and retains its character. and, in fact, so *detailed* and so to speak dramatic that I am obliged to give it the following titles. All[egr]o: Separation. *Adagio*, Lament. *Finale*. highest pain, consolation, reunion jubilation.

Since I very much hate all captioned musical pictures, it makes me infernally angry getting used to this idea, and yet it keeps irresistibly urging me on and wants to convince me of its effectiveness. in any case, I do not want to appear with it initially at any place where I am not known, for fear of being misunderstood and reckoned as being amongst the musical *charlatans*.'

The earliest evidence of the project's implementation is given by Weber's diary entry of 28 February 1821, noting the conclusion of the definitive conception of the work: ('completely conceived'). Further work stages then followed in May and June 1821 during the rehearsal phase for the first performance of his *Freischütz* in Berlin. Weber recorded the conclusion of the composition, i.e., the completion of the first autograph score, in his diary on 18 June 1821, the day of the *Freischütz* première in Berlin ('completed').

Whether and how Weber retained the original narrative conception can no longer be reconstructed today, since no other statements of his about this are extant, and the *Konzertstück* shows no comparable "titles" – apart from the characterising adjectives of the original tempo markings 'Larghetto affettuoso (b. 1), 'Allegro passionato' (b. 86) and 'Presto: giojoso' (b. 305), that were partly altered in the first print appearing in 1823. Nevertheless, the first reviews of the piece already allude to a plot structure that can be imagined in parallel with the music and that is, above all, emotionally defined, which is similar, at least in its basic features, to Weber's original idea. For example, the *Zeitung für Theater und Musik* wrote on the occasion of Weber's first public performance of the work in the Berlin Schauspielhaus on 25 June 1821:[1]

'Herr v. Weber had first devised a new C o n c e r t P i e c e for the p i a n o f o r t e with orchestral accompaniment during his local presence, taking into account the taste of the time for s h o r t e r pieces, whilst at the same time still including the main genres of concert music, with much originality and, as it were, as a psychological tone painting, which in its *Larghetto effettuoso* [sic] (in *F minor*), seems to express the yearning pain of feminine lament over the separation from the Beloved. The pain grows to despair in the *Allegro passionato,* and finally falls silent after the wildest outbursts of excited passion. In softly sustaining bassoon tones the distant call of the returning lover sounds, in the soft opening and growing to the greatest strength of the instruments, the brilliant *Alla Marcia* will indicate the real return, followed by the *Rondo giojoso* surging in the joy of the reunion.'

Thus the account transmitted by Julius Benedict long after Weber's death, that the composer played his work to his wife Caroline and himself on 18 June 1821, the day of the Berlin première of the *Freischütz*, and connected it with a story about a woman's longing for her absent husband, her grief over his presumed death and her joy at his unexpected return, may probably be based on a true incident:[2]

'Fortunately, she [Caroline von Weber] felt much better, and Weber was so delighted by this favourable change that he played the concert piece finished the same morning to both of us! –
– "The wife at the castle sits on the balcony and gazes wistfully out into the far distance; the knight has been in the Holy Land for years – will she ever see him again, the beloved companion? – Many bloody battles are fought. – No message from him who is her all. In vain, her pleading and begging, in

vain her yearning for the great lord. – Finally, she is gripped by despair and horror – he lies on the battlefield, abandoned by his own – his lifeblood flowing from the wound. – Oh, could I but help him and at least die with him! – She sinks unconscious and exhausted – Hark, – what is sounding in the distance?! – What glitters in the forest in the sunshine?! – What is coming closer and closer? The stately knights and squires – all with the sign of the cross – and waving flags – and people's jubilation – and there – It is he! And now rushing into his arms – what a wave of love – what endless indescribable happiness – how it is wafting, rushing with bliss from the branches and waves – proclaiming with a thousand voices the triumph of faithful courtly love. –".'

The present music text is based on the edition of the *Konzertstück* in Weber's *Sämtliche Werke* [Complete Works], series V, vol. 5 (Mainz: Schott, 2018), edited by M. Bandur. The edition follows the first print of the parts as the main source; additionally, it was possible to use Weber's first autograph score as a photocopy for the first time, thereby allowing the music text of the first edition that underlies all former editions to be checked for possible errors and readings and corrected when necessary. Additions from this source were given in parentheses. Editorial additions are in square brackets. Merely the editorially-added accidentals were printed in grey due to lack of space. Detailed information on the genesis, publication and early reception as well as sources and editions of the work can be found in the relevant volume of the *Sämtliche Werke*.

Markus Bandur
Translation: Margit L. McCorkle

[1] *Zeitung für Theater und Musik zur Unterhaltung gebildeter, unbefangener Leser. Eine Begleiterinn des Freimüthigen*, vol. 1, no. 26 (30 June 1821), 102.
[2] Quoted from Friedrich Wilhelm Jähns's copy of Benedict's letter to Max Maria von Weber of 8 August 1861 (in: *D-B*, Weberiana Cl. V [Mappe XIX], Abt. 5A, Nr. 5a, 17f.). Cf. also Benedict, *Weber. New Edition*, London, 1881, 65f.

VORWORT

Webers *Konzertstück* für Klavier und Orchester kommt sowohl im Œuvre des Komponisten als auch in der Gattungsgeschichte des romantischen Klavierkonzerts eine Sonderstellung zu. Dies hängt nicht nur mit den hohen spieltechnischen Ansprüchen an den Pianisten zusammen, sondern auch mit dem neuartigen Ausdruckscharakter und in besonderem Maße mit der aus einer programmatischen Idee heraus entwickelten musikalisch-poetischen Form.

Die Abhängigkeit der individuellen Formgestaltung von einer programmatischen Idee findet sich um 1820 zwar ebenfalls – wenn auch in deutlich geringerem Maße – in Werken etwa von Louis Spohr, Daniel Steibelt, John Field und Ferdinand Ries. Doch wurde insbesondere Webers *Konzertstück* im 19. und – bezieht man die formale Gestalt von Igor Stravinskys *Capriccio* für Klavier und Orchester mit ein – auch im 20. Jahrhundert zum Anknüpfungspunkt für die Auflösung der standardisierten zyklischen Form und für die Ausprägung der einsätzigen Konzertform.

Schon kurz nachdem Weber Anfang März 1815 die Belegexemplare seines zweiten Klavierkonzerts erhalten hatte, trug er sich bereits mit dem Gedanken an ein weiteres, drittes Konzert für Klavier und Orchester in f-Moll. Aufschlussreich sind in diesem Zusammenhang seine über dieses Projekt hinausreichenden Überlegungen zur Verwendung von Molltonarten in Konzertwerken und zur Programmmusik im Allgemeinen in einem Brief an Friedrich Rochlitz vom 14. März 1815. Zwar macht sein Schreiben deutlich, dass er kein Anhänger der „betitelten Tonbilder", d. h. der Programmmusik, sei und ihre Vertreter gar als ‚musikalische Scharlatane' bewerte. Allerdings ist er der Ansicht, dass Konzerte in Moll weniger wirkungsvoll seien als solche in Dur. Aus diesem Grund hoffe er, dass die sich ihm bei seinen kompositorischen Planungen für das dritte Klavierkonzert „aufdrängende" Erzählung, d. h. die

dem Stück in Form von expliziten „Titeln" unterlegte „Art Geschichte", diesen Nachteil beim Publikum ausgleiche:

„ich habe jezt ein *Clavier Concert* in *F moll* im Plan. da aber die *moll Concerte* ohne bestimmte erwekende Idee beym Publikum selten wirken, so hat sich so ganz seltsam in mir unwillkührlich dem Ganzen eine Art Geschichte untergeschoben, nach deren Faden die Stükke sich reihen, und ihren Charakter erhalten. und zwar so *detaillirt* und gleichsam dramatisch daß ich mich genöthigt sehen werde ihnen folgende Titel zu geben. <u>Allo: Trennung</u>. *Adagio*, Klage. *Finale*. höchster <u>Schmerz</u>, <u>Trost</u>, <u>Wiedersehen</u> <u>Jubel</u>. Da ich alle betitelten Tonbilder sehr haße, so wird es mir höllisch sauer mich selbst an diese Idee zu gewöhnen, und doch drängt sie sich mir unwiderstehlich immer wieder auf und will mich von Ihrer Wirksamkeit überzeugen. auf jeden Fall möchte ich an keinem Orte wo man mich nicht schon kennt damit zuerst auftreten, aus Furcht, verkannt und unter die Musikal: *Charlatans* gerechnet zu werden."

Den frühesten Hinweis auf die Umsetzung von Webers Vorhaben gibt der Tagebucheintrag vom 28. Februar 1821, in dem Weber die Fertigstellung der definitiven Konzeption des Werks vermerkte („vollendet Gedacht"). Weitere Arbeitsschritte folgten dann im Mai und Juni 1821 während der Probenphase zur ersten Aufführung seines *Freischütz* in Berlin. Den Abschluss der Komposition, d. h. die Beendigung der schriftlichen Partiturniederschrift notierte Weber im Tagebuch am 18. Juni 1821, am Tag der Uraufführung des *Freischütz* in Berlin („<u>vollendet</u>").

Ob und wie Weber an der ursprünglichen narrativen Konzeption festhielt, lässt sich heute nicht mehr rekonstruieren, da von ihm selbst keine weiteren Äußerungen dazu überliefert sind und das *Konzertstück* keine vergleichbaren „Titel" aufweist – sieht man einmal von den charakterisierenden Adjektiven der ursprünglichen, im 1823 erschienenen Erstdruck aber teilweise geänderten Tempobezeichnungen

„Larghetto affettuoso" (T. 1), „Allegro passionato" (T. 86) und „Presto: giojoso" (T. 305) ab. Allerdings enthalten schon die ersten Besprechungen des Stücks Anspielungen auf ein zur Musik parallel imaginierbares und vor allem in emotionaler Hinsicht definiertes Handlungsgerüst, das zumindest in den Grundzügen Gemeinsamkeiten mit Webers ursprünglicher Idee aufweist. So heißt es etwa anlässlich der ersten öffentlichen Aufführung des Werks durch Weber im Berliner Schauspielhaus am 25. Juni 1821:[1]

„Ein neues Concert-Stück für das Pianoforte mit Orchester-Begleitung hatte Hr. v. Weber erst während seiner hiesigen Anwesenheit, mit Berücksichtigung des Zeit Geschmacks an kürzeren, und dennoch die Haupt-Gattungen der Concert-Musik umfassenden Sätzen, mit vieler Originalität und gleichsam als ein psychologisches Ton-Gemälde erfunden, welches im *Larghetto effettuoso* [sic] (in *F moll*) den sehnsuchtsvollen Schmerz weiblicher Klage über die Trennung von dem Geliebten auszudrücken scheint. Der Schmerz wächst in dem *Allegro passionato* bis zur Verzweiflung an, und verstummt endlich nach den wildesten Ausbrüchen aufgeregter Leidenschaft. Da ertönt in sanft getragenen Fagott-Tönen der entfernte Ruf des wiederkehrenden Geliebten, in dem leise beginnenden und bis zur größten Stärke der Instrumente anwachsenden, brillanten *Alla Marcia* wird die wirkliche Rückkehr angedeutet, dem das in Freude des Wiedersehens wogende *Rondo giojoso* sich anschließt."

So mag die Schilderung von Julius Benedict, dass Weber seiner Frau Caroline und ihm am 18. Juni 1821, dem Tag der Berliner Uraufführung des *Freischütz*, das Werk vorgespielt und dies mit einer Geschichte über die Sehnsucht einer Frau nach ihrem abwesenden Gemahl, ihrer Trauer über seinen vermuteten Tod und ihrer Freude über seine unerwartete Rückkehr verknüpft habe, durchaus auf einer wahren Begebenheit beruhen:[2]

„Glücklicherweise fühlte sie [sc. Caroline von Weber] sich viel besser, und Weber war so erfreut über diese günstige Änderung, daß er uns beiden, das an demselben Morgen vollendete Concertstück vorspielte! –

– ,Die Burgfrau sitzt auf dem Söller, und schaut wehmüthig in die weite Ferne hinaus; der Ritter ist seit Jahren im heiligen Lande – wird sie ihn wiedersehen, den geliebten Lebensgefährten? – Viele blutige Schlachten sind geschlagen. – Keine Botschaft von ihm, der ihr Alles ist. Vergebens ihr Flehn und Bitten, vergebens ihre Sehnsucht nach dem hohen Herrn. – Endlich ergreift sie Verzweiflung und Entsetzen – er liegt auf dem Schlachtfeld, verlassen von den Seinen – das Herzblut aus der Wunde rinnend. – Ach könnte ich ihm zur Seite sein – und wenigstens mit ihm sterben! – Sie sinkt bewußtlos u. erschöpft hin – Horch – was klingt dort in der Ferne?! – Was glänzt im Wald im Sonnenschein?! – Was kommt näher und näher? Die stattlichen Ritter u. Knappen – alle mit dem Kreuzeszeichen – und wehenden Fahnen – und VolksJubel – und dort – Er ist's! – und nun in seine Arme stürzend – welch ein Wogen der Liebe – welch endloses unbeschreibliches Glück – wie weht, rauscht es mit Wonne aus den Zweigen u. Wellen – mit tausend Stimmen den Triumph treuer Minne verkündend –'."

Der Notentext basiert auf der Ausgabe des *Konzertstücks* in Webers *Sämtlichen Werken*, Serie V, Bd. 5 (Mainz: Schott, 2018), hg. von M. Bandur. Die Edition folgt dem Stimmenerstdruck als Hauptquelle; dabei konnte erstmals auf eine Fotokopie der ersten autographen Partiturniederschrift Webers zurückgegriffen werden und dadurch der den bisherigen Ausgaben zugrundeliegende Notentext des Erstdrucks auf eventuelle Fehler und Verlesungen überprüft und gegebenenfalls korrigiert werden. Ergänzungen nach dieser Quelle wurden mit runden Klammern versehen, Herausgeberergänzungen stehen in eckigen Klammern. Lediglich die vom Herausgeber ergänzten Akzidentien wurden aus Platzgründen durch Grausatz vom übrigen Notentext abgehoben. Ausführliche Angaben zur Entstehungsgeschichte, Drucklegung und frühen Rezeption sowie zu den Quellen und zur Edition des Werks enthält der genannte Band der *Sämtlichen Werke*.

Markus Bandur

---

[1] *Zeitung für Theater und Musik zur Unterhaltung gebildeter, unbefangener Leser. Eine Begleiterin des Freimüthigen*, Jg. 1, Nr. 26 (30. Juni 1821), S. 102.

[2] Zit. nach der Abschrift von Benedicts Brief an Max Maria von Weber vom 8. August 1861 durch Friedrich Wilhelm Jähns (in: *D-B*, Weberiana Cl. V [Mappe XIX], Abt. 5A, Nr. 5a, S. 17f.). Vgl. auch Benedict, *Weber. New Edition*, London 1881, S. 65f.

KONZERTSTÜCK

Carl Maria von Weber
(1786–1826)
WeV N.17

Edited by Markus Bandur
© 2019 Ernst Eulenburg Ltd, London
and Ernst Eulenburg & Co GmbH, Mainz

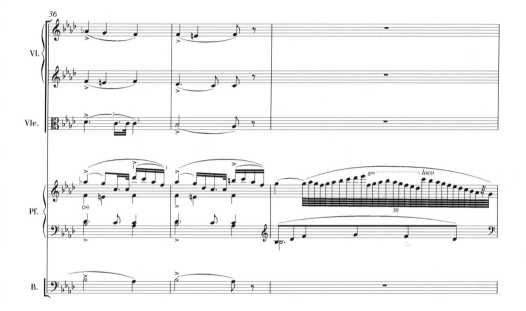

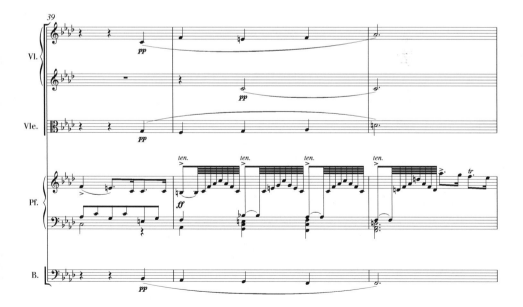

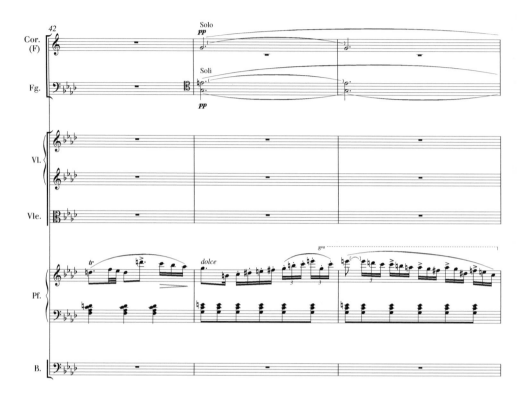

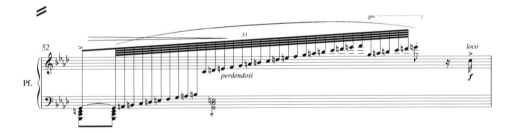

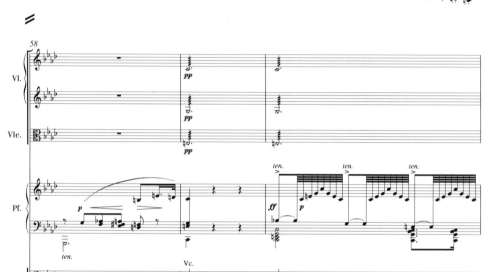

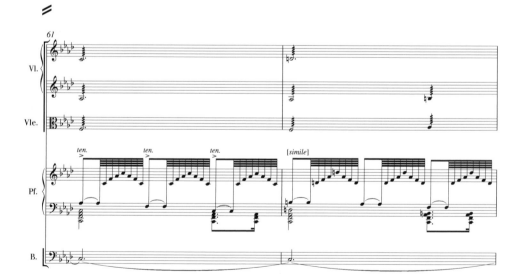

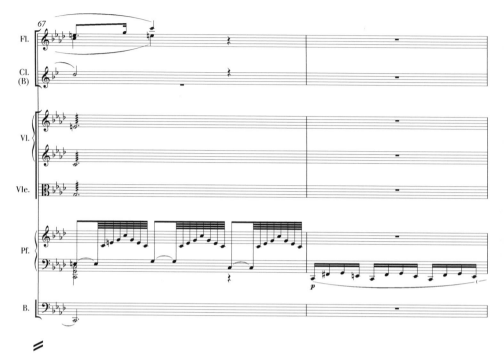

poco a poco più moto.   a piacere

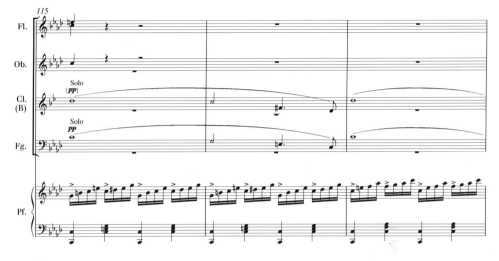

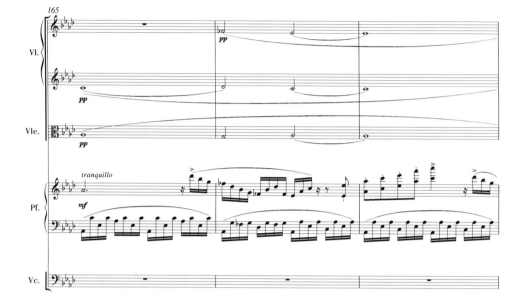

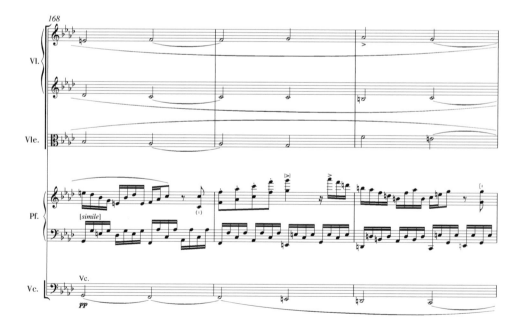

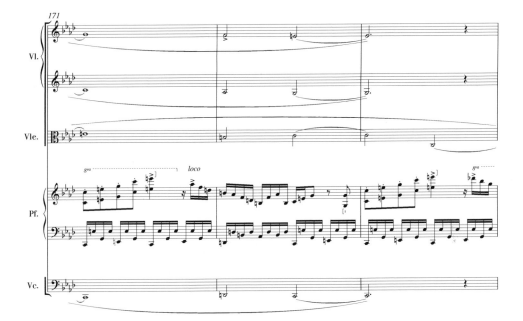

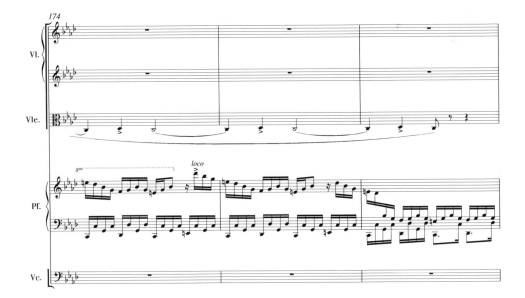

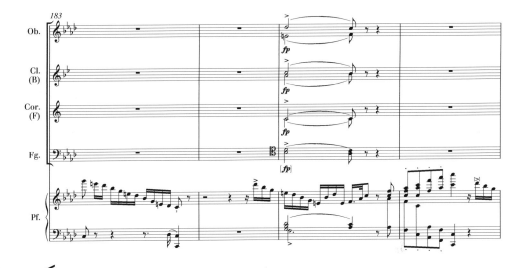

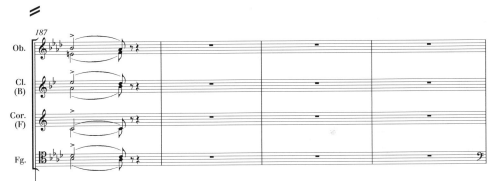

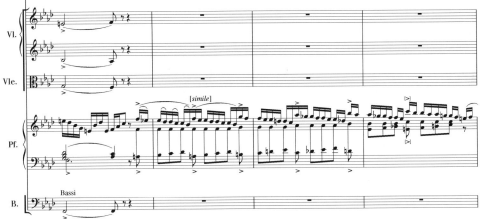

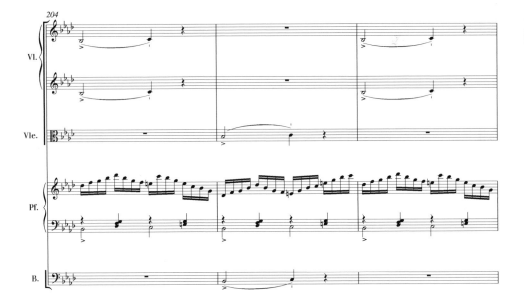

36

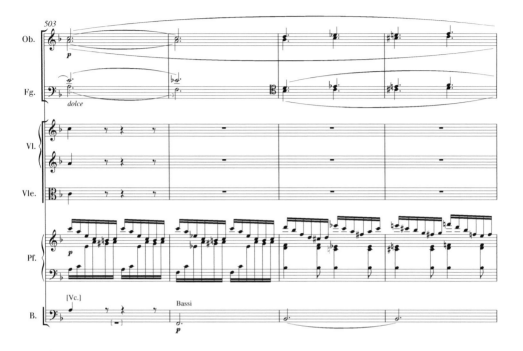

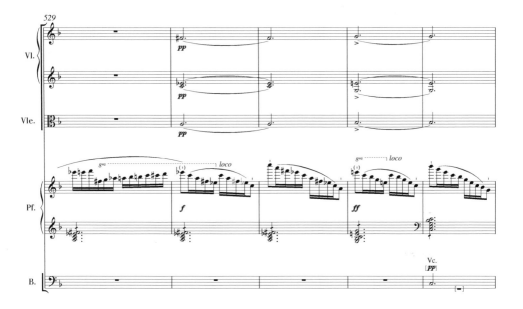

FINE.